DIFFERENT IS
SUPER!

RAE'S FIRST DAY

The first story in THE CAPABLES series

Created and Written by
Danny Jordan

Illustrated by
Agustina Perciante

Published by
The Capables LLC

Edited by
Alex Asher Sears

FOR EMERSON ROSE, YOUR LIGHT IS A GIFT TO THE WORLD.
SHINE BRIGHT, KIDDO.
-DAD

Library of Congress Control Number: 2021900314

ISBN 978-1-7364580-0-6 (hardback)
10 9 8 7 6 5 4 3 2

ISBN 978-1-7364580-1-3 (paperback)
ISBN 978-1-7364580-2-0 (ebook)

Printed and bound in the United States of America
First Edition, March 2021

Edited by Alex Asher Sears
Book design by Danny Jordan and Agustina Perciante
Publisher: The Capables LLC

Website: www.thecapables.com
Social Media: @thecapables

IT WAS A DAY LIKE ANY OTHER...
...YET IT FELT DIFFERENT FROM ANY DAY RAE HAD EXPERIENCED BEFORE.

A BOWL FULL OF PUFFY CEREAL SAT ON THE TABLE IN FRONT OF HER.
THE TRUSTY FAMILY PUP SAT ANXIOUSLY, HOPING FOR JUST ONE SCRUMPTIOUS PUFF TO DROP TO THE FLOOR.

AND, JUST LIKE EVERY OTHER DAY, EVERY OTHER TIME HE HAD SAID THE WORD **CAPABLE...** A JOLT RAN THROUGH HER.

RAE HAD NEVER MENTIONED THE JOLT TO THEM... OR HER POWER. CAPABLE WAS ACTUALLY MORE THAN JUST A WORD. IT WAS SOMETHING VERY REAL, VERY POWERFUL...AND KIND OF SCARY.

MAYBE I SHOULD FINALLY JUST TELL THEM...

...HMM...

...NOPE.

THERE WAS ALREADY SO MUCH GOING ON TODAY; IT WAS HER FIRST DAY OF SCHOOL.
TO DO:
-PACK LUNCH
-PACK
RAE'S
ADDING TO THE EXCITEMENT WAS THE LAST THING SHE WANTED TO DO.

...YOU ARE STRONG, YOU ARE CAPABLE!
DAD, YOU KNOW I KNOW ALL OF THESE THINGS. WHY DO YOU REPEAT THEM OVER AND OVER AGAIN?

WHY DO YOU THINK I REPEAT THEM OVER AND OVER AGAIN?
BECAUSE YOU WANT ME TO KNOW THE POWER I POSSESS.
AND THAT MY VALUE IS TIED TO MORE THAN JUST ONE THING.
YOU WANT ME TO KNOW THAT MY DIFFERENCES ARE WHAT MAKE ME UNIQUE.

RAE KNEW THAT SHE WAS CAPABLE, BUT HER PARENTS HAD NO IDEA OF THE HIDDEN POWER SHE POSSESSED.
IF ONLY THEY KNEW JUST HOW CAPABLE SHE WAS. IF ONLY HER DAD KNEW JUST HOW TRUE HIS WORDS WERE.

RAE'S DIFFERENCE DIDN'T JUST MAKE HER UNIQUE.
HER DIFFERENCE...IT MADE HER SUPER.

WRAPPED UP IN THOUGHT, SHE ALMOST DIDN'T HEAR HER MOM CALL...
RAE! C'MON, GRAB YOUR BACKPACK.

THE TIME HAD COME. IT WAS TIME TO LEAVE FOR SCHOOL.
California
10ERJ18
ALL OF A SUDDEN, THIS GREAT POWER RAE POSSESSED DIDN'T SEEM SO SUPER.
THE FEAR OF GOING TO SCHOOL FOR THE FIRST TIME EVER, IT FELT TOO BIG.

JUST THEN, HER DAD SWOOPED HER UP AND FLEW HER TO THE CAR AND, FOR THAT MOMENT, THE FEAR FLEW AWAY, TOO.

California
10ERJ18

THE RAIN SPAT FROM THE SKY, VILLAINOUS, POUNDING AGAINST THE WINDSHIELD AS THE FAMILY CAR ROLLED THROUGH TOWN TOWARDS RAE'S SCHOOL.
CLICK!
CARRAACK
MAYBE THEY'LL JUST CANCEL SCHOOL.
HA! WOULDN'T THAT BE SPECTACULAR!
WE'D JUST DRIVE TO SOMEWHERE FAR AWAY AND HAVE AN AWESOME ADVENTURE.

NOT. HAPPENING.
WAAAH.

THE REALITY OF AN ALREADY SCARY DAY GETTING EVEN WORSE STARTED TO SINK IN.

HOW WILL WE EVEN GET TO PLAY OUTSIDE IF IT'S RAINING?
YOU'LL PLAY INSIDE...
IT WON'T BE THAT BAD.
AND REMEMBER, WE TALKED ABOUT ALL THE WAYS YOU CAN ENJOY INDOOR RECESS - PLAYING WITH PUZZLES, READING A BOOK, OR ENJOYING ARTS AND CRAFTS.

RAE LIKED PUZZLES AND ART, BUT SHE LOVED THE OUTDOORS. FOR HER, OUTSIDE WAS WHERE THE FUN WAS, WHERE THE ADVENTURE LIVED, WHERE THE SKY WASN'T EVEN THE LIMIT.
AS THEY PULLED UP TO THE FRONT OF THE SCHOOL, ALL OF THE KIDS AND PARENTS WERE RUSHING INSIDE TO ESCAPE THE POWERFUL RAIN THAT SHOWERED DOWN ON THEM.
DART ELEMENTARY SCHOOL
WELCOME BAC
STUDENTS!
BUS

I NEED TO DO SOMETHING ABOUT THIS.
WHAT WAS THAT, HONEY?

RAE KNEW SHE COULD TALK TO HER PARENTS ABOUT ANYTHING, BUT SHE DECIDED THIS WASN'T THE TIME.

I SAID...
I'M SO...
EXCITED ABOUT THIS.

HER MOM AND DAD KNEW SOMETHING WAS UP, BUT WITH A SHARED GLANCE, THEY LET IT GO.

THEY ALL TOOK A DEEP BREATH TOGETHER, EXHALED, WHIPPED OPEN THEIR DOORS, AND MADE A MAD DASH FOR THE FRONT ENTRANCE TO THE SCHOOL.

WHEN THEY ARRIVED AT THE CLASSROOM DOOR, THERE WAS A FLURRY OF NOISE.

THE TEACHER, MISS MEEK, WALKED OVER AND INVITED RAE INSIDE.

SHE REACHED FOR RAE'S RIGHT HAND.
RAE QUICKLY PULLED AWAY.

YOU SEE...

NOT ONLY WAS THIS RAE'S FIRST DAY OF SCHOOL, THIS WAS THE FIRST TIME RAE'S SUPERPOWER COULD POSSIBLY BE REVEALED TO OTHERS. SHE WAS SCARED OF HOW PEOPLE WOULD REACT.

RAE'S PARENTS' FEARS WERE DIFFERENT, HOWEVER. THEY WERE NERVOUS ABOUT RAE BEING OUT ON HER OWN, WITHOUT THEM, FOR THE FIRST TIME.

THOUGH RAE WAS ABLE TO KEEP HER SUPERPOWER SUPER SECRET, HER RIGHT ARM WAS NOT LIKE EVERYONE ELSE'S, AND OTHERS OFTEN POINTED IT OUT.

WHILE MOST KIDS ARE BORN WITH TWO BONES IN EACH FOREARM, RAE WAS BORN WITH ONLY ONE BONE IN HER RIGHT FOREARM. BECAUSE OF THIS, HER RIGHT ARM WAS SHORTER THAN HER LEFT, AND HER HAND HAD TWO FINGERS.

IT WASN'T STRANGE TO RAE BECAUSE IT WAS ALL SHE KNEW.
IT ONLY SEEMED TO BE SOMETHING THAT OTHER PEOPLE CARED ABOUT.

MOMMY, DADDY,
I DON'T WANT TO DO THIS.

WHAT HAVE WE ALWAYS SAID?

RAE THOUGHT TO HERSELF CONFIDENTLY.
I AM SMART, I AM STRONG,
I AM CAPABLE, I AM A WARRIOR.

BUT AS SHE LOOKED
AROUND THE BUSTLING
CLASSROOM, HER HEART
BEGAN TO RACE.

I AM DIFFERENT.
YES, AND
WHAT ELSE?

SOME PEOPLE WILL LOOK AT ME DIFFERENTLY, AND THAT'S OKAY.
WE'RE ALL DIFFERENT, AND IT'S OUR INDIVIDUAL DIFFERENCES AND EXPERIENCES THAT MAKE OUR WORLD **SUPER.**

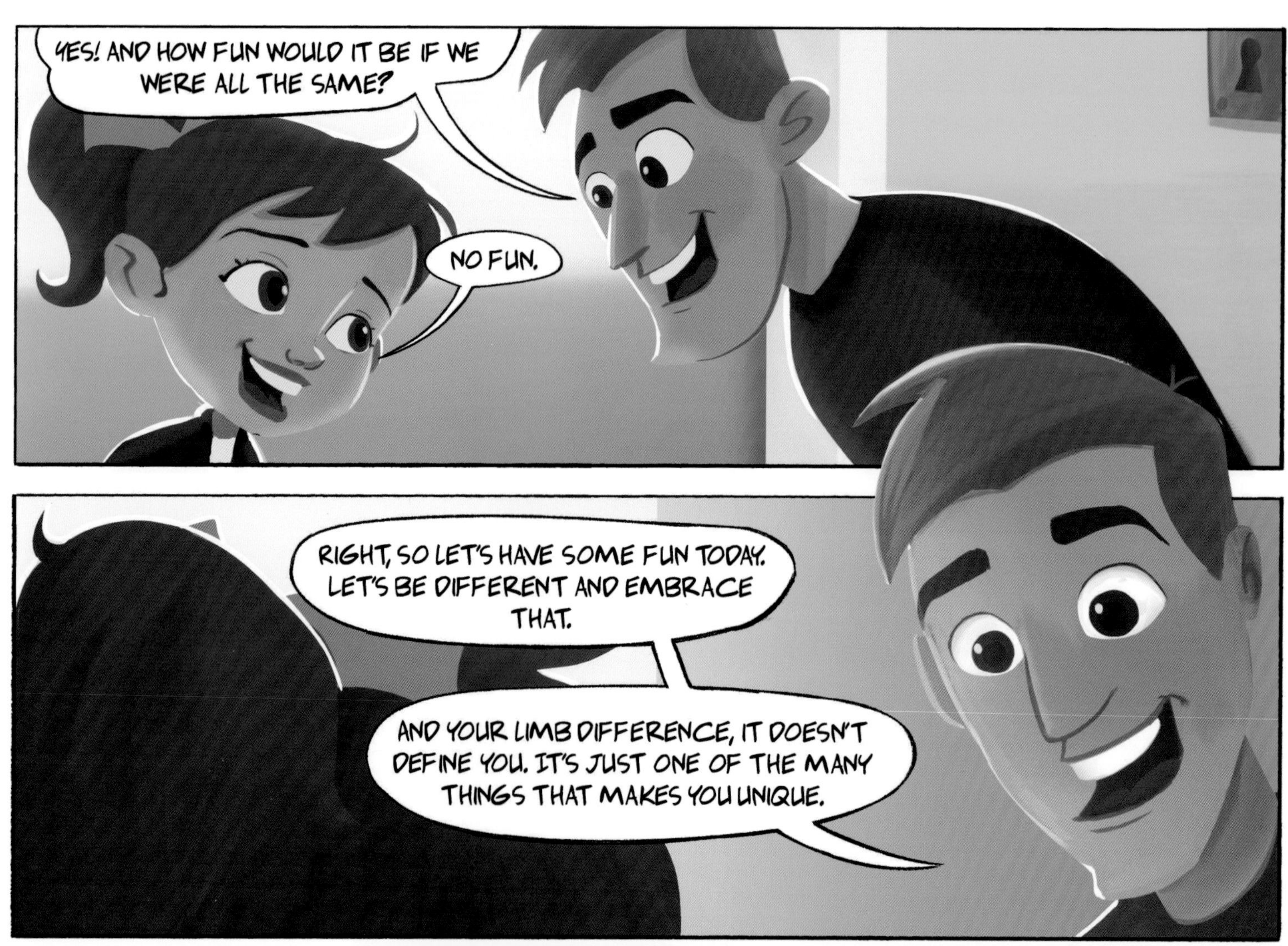
YES! AND HOW FUN WOULD IT BE IF WE WERE ALL THE SAME?
NO FUN.
RIGHT, SO LET'S HAVE SOME FUN TODAY. LET'S BE DIFFERENT AND EMBRACE THAT.
AND YOUR LIMB DIFFERENCE, IT DOESN'T DEFINE YOU. IT'S JUST ONE OF THE MANY THINGS THAT MAKES YOU UNIQUE.

SHE KNEW HE WAS RIGHT.

BUT STILL...

...KIDS CAN BE MEAN.

JUST THEN A COUPLE CLASSMATES RAN OVER TO RAE, POINTING AT HER.

THE KIDS LOOKED AT HER CURIOUSLY.

WHAT HAPPENED TO YOUR ARM?
I WAS BORN THIS WAY.

AND IT'S OUR DIFFERENCES THAT MAKE US SUPER.

THAT'S RIGHT!
DO YOU WANT TO COME PLAY WITH US?

YES!

RAE GAVE HER MOM AND DAD A QUICK HUG AND SHE WAS OFF.

HER MOM AND DAD WATCHED WITH GREAT PRIDE AS RAE RAN OUT INTO THE WORLD, ON HER OWN.

WITH ONE BIG CHALLENGE OVERCOME,
RAE WAS FEELING CALMER.

THE MORNING WAS PACKED WITH FUN ACTIVITIES AND LESSONS...
FIND THE WORDS

...BUT AS RECESS GREW CLOSER, THE MOOD IN THE CLASSROOM CHANGED.

THE RAIN WAS STILL POUNDING DOWN OUTSIDE, AND THEIR PLAYGROUND WAS LOOKING MORE LIKE A WATERPARK THAN ANYTHING ELSE.

I'M SORRY TO REPORT THAT RECESS WILL BE INSIDE TODAY, KIDS.
AWW...

UPON HEARING THE KIDS' DISAPPOINTMENT, RAE FELT THE SAME ENERGY SHE HAD EXPERIENCED AT HOME CREEPING UP INSIDE OF HER AGAIN.

MAYBE THIS IS THE TIME.

TIME FOR WHAT?
RAE HADN'T REALIZED SHE WAS THINKING OUT LOUD.

BUT RAE TRUSTED LEX FOR SOME REASON, A REASON SHE COULDN'T EXPLAIN YET.
IT'S TIME FOR ME TO SHARE WHAT REALLY MAKES ME DIFFERENT.
RIIIIGHT.

WHAT I'M ABOUT TO DO, NOBODY WOULD EVER IMAGINE I CAN DO.
THE STARES I GET FROM OTHERS...
THE QUESTIONS ABOUT MY ARM - IT'S ALL ENERGY, AND I CAN USE IT IN A SUPER POWERFUL WAY.

MMM-KAY.

IN THE BLINK OF AN EYE, RAE BOLTED TO THE BACK OF THE ROOM AND SLID BEHIND THE BOOKSHELVES.
WHOOOSH!

WHAT HAPPENED NEXT COULD NOT BE DISGUISED BY THE TALL SHELVES SHE ATTEMPTED TO HIDE HERSELF BEHIND.

WHOOOOOOOM

IT WAS IMPOSSIBLE TO TELL.

JUST AS QUICKLY AS THE BLAZE OF LIGHT APPEARED, IT WAS GONE, AND SO WAS THE RAIN.
THE CLOUDS PARTED, AND THE SUN BEGAN TO PEEK THROUGH. THE SUN GREW BRIGHTER, QUICKLY DRYING UP THE WATER, ALMOST AS IF IT HAD BEEN COMMANDED TO DO SO.

THE STUDENTS LOOKED ON, STUNNED, NOT UNDERSTANDING WHAT THEY HAD JUST SEEN.

MISS MEEK'S JAW WAS PRACTICALLY ON THE FLOOR.

OK, CLASS...
I, UH...
...GUESS WE'RE HAVING RECESS OUTSIDE TODAY.

YAAAAAAY!

RAE SMILED AS HER CLASSMATES
ALL RUSHED OUT TO THE PLAYGROUND.
D

WELCOME

OUTSIDE, LEX AND RAE FLOATED BACK AND FORTH, SIDE BY SIDE, ON THE SWINGS.

WHEW, THAT WORKED OUT WAY BETTER THAN I EXPECTED.
YEAH...
THAT WAS... WOWZA.
I DIDN'T THINK OTHER PEOPLE HAD THOSE POWERS.

OTHER PEOPLE?

YEAH...
I MEAN....
I THOUGHT ONLY SUPERHEROES IN MOVIES COULD DO THOSE SORTS OF THINGS.

SURPRISE!

DO YOUR PARENTS KNOW?
NO. WAY.
ARE YOU GOING TO TELL THEM?

I WILL TELL THEM... SOMEDAY. BUT, FOR NOW, I'M PERFECTLY CONTENT KNOWING THAT MY DIFFERENCE MADE A DIFFERENCE.

THAT NIGHT, A SUPERMOON DOMINATED THE SKY.

RAE GAZED OUT OF HER BEDROOM WINDOW AT THE MASSIVE GLOWING ORB.
AM I THE ONLY ONE?
ONE DAY SHE WOULD DISCOVER THAT THERE WERE, IN FACT, OTHER KIDS - **CAPABLES** LIKE HER - STARING AT THE SAME MOON, EAGER TO SHARE THEIR OWN UNIQUE SUPERPOWERS WITH THE WORLD.

TO BE CONTINUED...

ABOUT THE AUTHOR

DANNY JORDAN IS A PROUD HUSBAND AND DAD, AND LOVER OF SPORTS AND LIVE THEATER. WHEN HIS DAUGHTER WAS DIAGNOSED WITH AN UPPER LIMB DIFFERENCE IN 2018, HE BECAME AN ADVOCATE FOR INCLUSION AND ACCURATE REPRESENTATION OF DISABILITY IN MEDIA.

OUTSIDE OF THIS THRILLING NEW LITERARY ADVENTURE, DANNY HAS PRODUCED AND DIRECTED OVER 150 HOURS OF PRIMETIME MAJOR NETWORK AND CABLE TELEVISION PROGRAMMING. HE HAS ALSO WORKED EXTENSIVELY AS A BRANDED MEDIA EXECUTIVE AND SPONSOR PRODUCER, SECURING PARTNERSHIPS WITH AND SUCCESSFULLY INTEGRATING LEADING BRANDS INTO TRADITIONAL AND DIGITAL MEDIA. SELECT PRODUCING CREDITS INCLUDE: EXTREME MAKEOVER: HOME EDITION, BIGGEST LOSER, MASTERCHEF, DEAL OR NO DEAL, STORAGE WARS, AND PLAYBILL PRESENTS: THE BROADWAY CAST (TOP 100 APPLE PODCAST).

THE PREMIERE STORY IN THE CAPABLES SERIES IS DANNY'S FIRST TIME EVER WRITING A BOOK, AND IT IS HIS HOPE THAT THIS IS JUST THE BEGINNING FOR THIS SERIES.

FOLLOW DANNY ON INSTAGRAM @DANNYJORDAN

ABOUT THE ILLUSTRATOR

AGUSTINA PERCIANTE WAS BORN IN BUENOS AIRES, ARGENTINA. GROWING UP, SHE WOULD SPEND HOURS DRAWING CARTOONS. EVERYWHERE SHE WENT, SHE HAD A PENCIL IN HER HAND.

NOWADAYS, SHE IS A FULL-TIME ILLUSTRATOR AND NOT A DAY GOES BY WHEN SHE DOESN'T MAKE ART.

FOLLOW AGUSTINA ON INSTAGRAM @PERCIMA.ART

A NOTE FROM THE AUTHOR

EACH STORY IN THE SERIES AIMS TO ACCURATELY AND RESPONSIBLY REPRESENT DISABILITY. THE CAPABLES' ADVISORY BOARD PLAYS A VITAL ROLE IN ENSURING THE STORIES, ALONG WITH THE LANGUAGE AND ILLUSTRATIONS USED, ARE APPROPRIATE AND SUPPORT POSITIVE PROGRESS.

THE CAPABLES ADVISORY BOARD

NICOLE KELLY, RYAN HADDAD, KIZZI BARAZETTI, JASON SCHNEIDER, AND MIKA JAIN

LEARN MORE ABOUT OUR ADVISORY BOARD'S WORK AT WWW.THECAPABLES.COM

Acknowledgements

THE PREMIERE STORY IN THE CAPABLES SERIES WAS MADE POSSIBLE THROUGH A SUCCESSFUL KICKSTARTER CAMPAIGN. WE OWE A VERY SPECIAL THANK YOU TO THE FOLLOWING PEOPLE WHO SUPPORTED US AND MADE THIS DREAM A REALITY:

MICHAEL AND MARILYN "GRAMPY AND GRAMMY BEAR" HOLLANDER, ANDREW AND KELSEY HOLLANDER, LUCKY FIN PROJECT, PATRICK HINDS, THE NORTONS, CATHERINE A. SISK, LEXIS SEROT AND LITTLEWINS.COM , MICHAEL RODRIGUEZ, THE BORCHARD FAMILY, THE FALCO FAMILY, MISS MIRANDA, THE TOLLIVER FAMILY, THE QUARTARARO FAMILY, MATTHEW JORDAN, UNCLE STEVE AND AUNTIE TANIA, THE EPSTEINS, CAMERON-ROSE LAURIN AND FAMILY, PROUD AND HONORED COUSIN MICHAEL JENSEN, THOMAS BÄHLER, THE GALLOWAY FAMILY, PARKER SCHREIBER, BRIAN LEE, KARA LINDSAY, CHELSEY CRISP, GIO MESSALE, AUNT SUE AND UNCLE JIM, PEJMAN AND VALERIE MANSOURIAN, MICHAEL, JAIMIEE, AND MACKENZIE MELILLI, JAMES RING AND ROBERT LADUCA, JONATHAN ADAM HEIERMAN II, MADELINE HEIERMAN, AND JONATHAN ADAM HEIERMAN, STEPHEN SANTOS, DAVID NORTON, DAN AND HEATHER FLYNN, THE LOVE FAMILY, ALISON AND BRYAN FRIEDMAN, LEE HASTINGS, KELLY HEALY, THE SIMON FAMILY, DYLAN DEENEY, THE TIDD FAMILY, JOHN AND SHARON MILLER, THE FREDRICKSON FAMILY (COLE, EVAN, MALIA, AND DAN), MICHAEL GERMAN, DIANE SEARLESS, THE KADRICH FAMILY, THE LACY FAMILY (AZ), J.K. SULLIVAN, SCOTT GILBERT, JERRY LYNCH, TAYLOR GRACE SORICE, EMMETT AND ADLER COLE, ELLANOIR MAÉ LUTZ, CHRIS ROSS, ASHLEY RAMOS, ELISSA FRANCIS, CHRISTOPHER J. HANKE, MADY VILLAVICENCIO, JORDANA DESERNIA, TERRY WALLACE, SHIREEN JAFFER AND RAAID HOSSAIN, GRAMMIE AND GRANDPA UNDERWOOD, SAHIL SAINI, KELLY AND KAELYN MCCAMY BROWN, THE HORWITZ FAMILY, THE HARRYCHAPJACKS, AUDREY AND NORA NG, STEVEN TIMMONS, KIRK HYRE, THE ROSENBLUTH FAMILY, MICHELLE AND JIM O'CONNOR, BRYAN KADRICH, JULIE WHITE, HAYLEY WALTERS, AND KATIE PETTIT.

ADDITIONALLY, THE AUTHOR WOULD LIKE TO THANK THE FOLLOWING PEOPLE FOR THEIR TIME, SUPPORT, AND GUIDANCE THROUGHOUT THE CREATIVE PROCESS:

RHETT REESE, LARRY POWELL, NICOLE KELLY, RYAN J. HADDAD, JASON SCHNEIDER, MIKA JAIN, KIZZI BARAZETTI, BRANDI PASSANTE, CAMERON BRITTON, ANCHAL JOSEPH, BREEGAN JANE, CARRIE LOCKLYN, DARREN KEEFE, HAYLEY PODSCHUN, TIM DOLAN, MIA TIDWELL, DEBORAH BAKER JR., ALLI FORSYTHE, BEN CAMERON, ERIC PETERSEN, DAVID ALPERT, GEENA AGUILAR, KYLE MAUCH, ERIN HOLLANDER, AND RUTHIE FIERBERG.

AND, TO MY PATIENT, STRONG, AND BEAUTIFUL WIFE, LYNN - THANK YOU FOR THE WAY YOU SO FIERCELY LOVE AND CARE FOR OUR SUPER-CAPABLE KID, AND FOR ALWAYS ENCOURAGING ME TO KEEP GOING. YOUR LOVE AND SUPPORT ARE TWO OF THE GREATEST GIFTS I HAVE RECEIVED IN MY LIFE. I LOVE YOU.